God sent his Son, Jesus to live among us and to die for us to show us how much he loved every single person.

Draw a picture of Jesus

Good Friday is a special day. Why?

....

Are there any crosses in your Church?

....

Why is the cross so important to us?

....

Have you ever had a Hot Cross Bun?

....

Where are the Stations of the Cross in your Church?

....

Shall we follow the Stations and find out more about why Good Friday is such a special day?

Let us begin the story of

★ Good Friday: ★

1st Station

Jesus meets Pilate

Jesus' first stop on the way of the cross is the Governor's palace. Many Jewish leaders want Jesus out of the way. "Crucify him" they insist.
They influence Pilate the Governor to condemn Jesus to death. Can you see Pilate washing his hands in the Station at your church?
Jesus is condemned to die like a criminal even though he is a good man.
He is sad that people reject him and do not appreciate his teachings about loving God and our neighbour.
When he is condemned he doesn't get angry or fight back.
He accepts his fate.

Let us pray.

If I can help others by sharing their troubles, make me kind enough to reach out to them as you did.

I will help others by

......Being KIND...........

2nd Station

Jesus takes the cross

The Roman soldiers bring a large wooden cross for Jesus to carry. It is very heavy and rough. Though Jesus is tired, he reaches out and accepts the cross.

For Jesus, the cross stands for all the world's evil, hatred and cruelty. By his love he transforms this cross into a symbol of hope and salvation for us.
When we make the sign of the cross we should remember this cross which Jesus carried out of love for us.

Let us pray.
Dear Jesus, please help me to be truly sorry
when I have done wrong.
Show me how to behave
in home, in school and at play
in a way that follows your example of peace and love.

I am sorry for

....

3rd Station

Jesus falls

Jesus falls. He is very exhausted and the cross is very heavy.
Is there a soldier with a whip in this Station in your Church?

When we have difficult things to bear, such as worries or fears or sadness,
think of Jesus. He falls under the burden of his cross but then he gets up
and begins again. When we are able to get over our troubles and go on we are like Jesus.

Let us pray.

Dear Jesus, help us to follow you
by making a fresh start each day.
Help me to begin each day
in a cheerful and caring way
which will bring happiness
to others.

I will be kind to

....

4th Station

Jesus meets his mother

On the narrow roadway, Jesus turns the corner and looks ahead to see his mother. She reaches out to touch him.

Jesus knows how sad his mother is but he is comforted to know that she is there. Sometimes we don't want our parents to see us in trouble but we like to know that they are there to support us and love us when we are growing up.

Let us pray.

Dear Jesus help us to appreciate the love of our parents. May we be loving members of our families and support each other through sad and happy times. We pray for children who are growing up without mummies and daddies.

I pray especially for

....

5th Station

Simon helps Jesus

The soldiers notice that Jesus is very weak. He is staggering under the load. So, they pull a man from the crowd - a stranger called Simon of Cyrene - and force him to help Jesus carry the cross.

Simon didn't want to help at first. He just wanted to see what was going on. However, he did his best and soon was very glad to be helping Jesus.

Let us pray.

When we have to do things we do not like,
help us to accept the tasks
and do our best.
Help us to be kind and helpful,
especially to those
who are disabled, sick or elderly.

I will help

....

5

6th Station

Veronica wipes the face of Jesus

A woman named Veronica steps out from the crowd with towel. She wipes the face of Jesus.

When Veronica wipes the face of Jesus she risks being told off or pushed by the soldiers or laughed at by the crowd. Her love and kindness overcome her fears.

Let us pray.

Dear Jesus
help us not to be selfish.
May we be friends
to people who are unpopular
or people who are in trouble.
May we stand up for them.

I will be friends with

....

7th Station

Jesus falls again

The walk is only half over. Even with Simon's help Jesus falls again under the weight of the heavy cross. But he gets up and moves on.

Jesus is burdened with our sins and the sins of the world. But he wants to overcome these sins and forgive us all.

Let us pray.

Dear Jesus help us to persevere
to help you overcome the sins of the world.
We are your hands and feet on earth
doing good for others around us.
Don't let us give up.

I will try harder to

....

8th Station

Jesus meets some women

Now Jesus passes by a group of women from Jerusalem. They are weeping for him because he is suffering so much. Jesus tells them to weep for themselves and for their children because the cruel things that happen in the world will surely touch them just as they are affecting him.

The world can be cruel. Women and children are the first to suffer because of war and violence in their countries.

Let us pray.

Jesus, may we always try to help people in the world who need such things as food, clean water, safe housing, a peaceful environment, especially women and children. Help us contribute towards making the world less cruel.

I will be kind to

....

9th Station

Jesus falls a third time

Jesus has no more strength left. He has climbed a hill carrying his heavy cross. Again he falls and struggles to stand up again.

Jesus has chosen the way of the cross out of his love for us. The path of following Jesus is not an easy one. Many people have been killed in the past because they were followers of Jesus and there are martyrs in our own time who are persecuted by those who choose violence instead of the path of love offered by Jesus.

Let us pray

for all those who have been a faithful witness to the teachings of Jesus. May their lives be an inspiration to us. We pray for those Christians persecuted today in some countries in the world.

I will pray for Christians in

....

10th Station

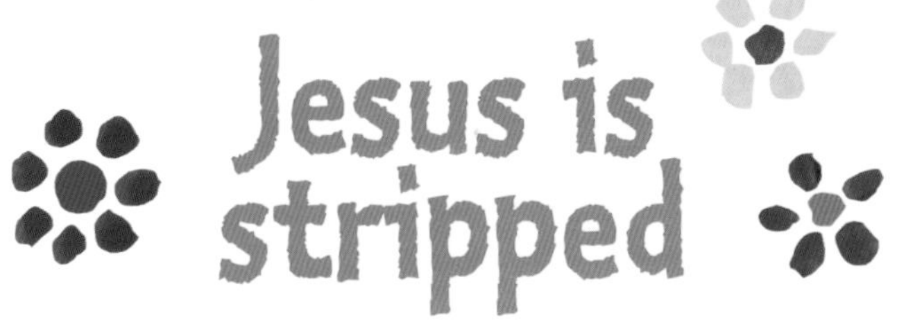

Jesus is stripped

Jesus has reached the top of the hill. He is allowed to put down the cross.
While Jesus stands in front of the crowds, the soldiers pull off his clothes.

Jesus is treated as if he were worthless and is left standing embarrassed and humiliated. When we have plasters taken off cuts we know how it hurts. When the soldiers pull off Jesus's clothes it must really hurt him but he is very brave.

Let us pray.

Dear Jesus
help us to be brave like you.
May we never be spiteful
to others who hurt us.
Help us always
to be peacemakers.

I will make peace with

....

11th Station

Jesus is nailed to the cross

The soldiers make Jesus lie down on the cross and they nail him to it. He is securely fastened. He cannot escape.

Whenever we are injured or sick in bed we remember Jesus who chose to die this way to show how much he loved the world. Jesus understands what it is like to feel trapped and to be in pain.

Let us pray.

Jesus, we pray for people
in our parish and local community,
or people we know elsewhere,
who are in pain or who are sick.
We remember those who are in hospital
today. Bring them comfort and relief.
Thank you for all carers who try to relieve
pain, such as doctors and nurses.

I will pray especially for

....

12th Station

Jesus dies

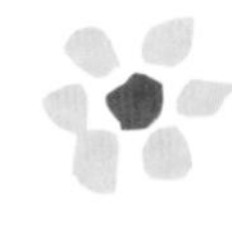

After hours of hanging on the cross, Jesus dies. Although it is daytime the sky turns dark. The earth shakes and a big crack appears in the temple in Jerusalem. Just before he dies, Jesus asks God to forgive those who are killing him. Then he says:

"Father, into your hands I commend my spirit".

Even in his last moments Jesus thinks of others. He gives us a wonderful example of gentleness and thoughtfulness despite his own suffering. Jesus teaches us how important it is to forgive and be reconciled to one another and to God.

Let us pray.

May we always recognise the presence of God in our lives.
Bless especially today those people who are dying and those who love them.

I recognise God in my life by

....

13th Station

Jesus is placed in the arms of Mary

Now that Jesus is dead, a few friends gently take him down from the cross and place him in the arms of his mother.

Mary held Jesus like this when he was a baby. But now there is no life left in him. How terrible she must have felt, remembering all the wonderful days she had spent with him. When we are sad because we have lost a relative or friend, Mary understands our loss and sadness.

Let us pray.

Jesus, we remember all mothers and fathers
who have lost their children
due to illness or injustice, violence or accident.
Let your mother Mary be a consoling influence
and help them to cope.

I am sorry for being unkind to

....

14th Station

Jesus is buried

The final resting place for Jesus is a tomb in a nearby garden. He is covered with cloth, placed inside and a stone is rolled across the entrance.

The friends of Jesus feel very discouraged
and they lose hope.
They think this is the end of the story of Jesus
and his teachings.
But we know better, don't we?

Let us pray.

May we learn to trust in God
when things seem to go wrong.
May your love be upon us O Lord
as we place all our hope in you.

Thank you God for sending your Son Jesus
to live among us and die for us.
Thank you for your love for humanity
and for your beautiful creation.

Lots of love

A...............................

My picture of Jesus